Grief Quest

A Workbook & Journal
To Heal The Grieving Heart

I. J. Weinstock

Grief Quest

A Workbook & Journal
To Heal The Grieving Heart

DreaMaster Books

For information:
DreaMaster Books
17130 Burbank Blvd.
Suite 302
Encino, CA 91316
DreaMasterBooks@gmail.com

Workbook page concept by Lea Tibbs

Book design services provided by
EditWriteDesign.com

Cover graphic by Juan Lucas

Waterbug & Dragonfly by Doris Stickney

Zallman Caps used with permission

PRAISE FOR GRIEF QUEST

*"**Grief Quest** is a wonderful workbook by the bereaved for the bereaved.*

In those very early years of the grief journey it is a challenge for young grievers to get through reading even a paragraph of text and remember what they just read. The intense grief overloads the frontal cortex of the brain and we have serious short term memory loss (CRS). This is why a workbook such as this is so valuable. It provides deep healing messages, quotes, stories, and questions/suggestions in a short and concise but meaningful way.

It provides a provocative road map and diary for the grieving soul; it does not pathologize, preach or instruct; it is a guided meditation in book form for the grieving heart. I would highly recommend this literal self help workbook for anyone on the grief journey."

— Mitch Carmody
author of *"Letters to My son, Turning Loss to Legacy"*

*"The **Grief Quest** workbook is GREAT...a real gem for those who are trying to navigate the path through grief."*

— Darcie D. Sims, Ph.D., CHT, CT, GMS
Director, American Grief Academy
Grief Inc.

*"**Grief Quest** is a well thought out journey for the bereaved who like to ponder and record their thoughts. Others may just want to dip in and out of the wonderful stories and ponder the soul-searching questions. Bereavement counselors and group facilitators could use the rich questions to stimulate discussion. Greif Quest's L.O.V.E. process can be very helpful to anyone who's lost a loved one."*

— Dr. Gloria Horsley, Grief Expert
President of The Open To Hope Foundation

*"**Grief Quest** is a powerful, and yet gentle journey into healing one of life's greatest wounds— the death of a loved one. Knowing that love is the only way through the pain, the author (who lost his beloved spouse) has skillfully devised a program for the grieving individual to draw on the love for the person they lost to soothe the aching heart."*

— Rabbi Mordechai Liebling, Reconstructionist Rabbinical College
(whose first wife died leaving four young children)

"We who experience the loss of a loved one need to become interpreters of our own grief. Your questions are a wonderful tool of discovery. Thank you."

— Reverend William Englund
First Baptist Church, St Paul, Minnesota

"I cannot tell you how much I loved **Grief Quest.** It definitely will be at the top of my list of journaling books to recommend at the workshop that I give each year at the national conference of The Compassionate Friends. I have many journaling books but this is, by far and away, the most well done. Kudos!!!"

— Cathy Seehuetter
TCF National Board of Directors
presenter of *Journaling as a Healing Tool* workshop

"I loved **Grief Quest.** What I particularly liked was the emphasis on positive emotions and experiences while also giving opportunity for the expression of pain and despair. Your book has tremendous potential for helping the bereaved through their grief. Well done!"

— Marcia F. Alig
Special Projects Coordinator, The Compassionate Friends

"Journaling can be such a healing part of a person's grief journey, and having such an organized and well thought out guide for this process is powerful. I believe that **Grief Quest** could serve as a wonderful healing tool for many in their grief."

— Glen Lord, The Grief Toolbox

For Joy,

Who lost two children, her only brother,
Her mother and several husbands,
Who taught me most of what I know about Love
And everything I know about Loss...
And who knew the importance of asking the right questions.

For My Mother & Father—Elsa & Mendel Weinstock,

Who, despite their unimaginable losses in the Holocaust,
Bequeathed to me unconditional love,
And modeled for me resiliency—
How to recreate a life that's been devastated,
And rise like the Phoenix again and again.

In Roman myth, Baucis and Philemon were an old married
couple who were favored by the gods and granted one wish.
Though poor, they didn't ask for wealth;
though old, they didn't ask for youth;
though infirm, they didn't ask for health.
Their one wish, above all others, was to die at the same time
so that neither would have to suffer the loss of the other
and go through the torments of grief.

"If you live to be a hundred,
I want to live to be a hundred minus one day
so I never have to live without you."

— A. A. Milne, author of *"Winnie-the-Pooh"*

*"It's the questions you ask
that determine the quest you take."*

— I. J. Weinstock

INTRODUCTION

The Questions Determine the Quest

When we are devastated by the loss of a loved one, we are plagued by questions. *"Why? How could this have happened? Where are you? Where did you go? What am I going to do? How am I going to live without you?"*

It is no accident that the word "quest" derives from the word "question." The quest to heal grief can be guided by asking the right questions. I know this from personal experience.

When I descended into the hell of grief after losing Joy, the love of my life, it was a question that saved me. A few weeks before Joy succumbed to breast cancer, she told me that if her death destroyed my life, then our love was a "poison pill." She made me promise that I wouldn't let that happen. That I would grieve only as much as necessary and not a second more. And that I would be open to a new life and new love even better than what we had. Not for my sake. For *her* sake.

They say *Love is the Answer*! Those who've experienced losing a loved one know that *Loss poses the Questions*. The first and most fundamental question Loss asks strikes at the very heart of love and grief—*Was our love a poison pill?*

When I was so depressed I could barely get out of bed, and so grief-stricken at losing Joy that I didn't care what happened to me, I remembered that question and the promise I made to her. I forced myself to seek out any blue sky, any silver lining, any ray of hope, any possibility of healing. For myself, I didn't give a damn. But for Joy I'd do anything, even heal my grief.

1

Perhaps the greatest obstacle to healing from the loss of a loved one is that we often unconsciously equate the degree of our suffering with the depth of our love. How can we give up our pain, if it's a testament to our love? To resolve this dilemma and navigate this paradox is what makes the *Grief Quest* a truly heroic undertaking.

Losing a loved one is probably life's most painful ordeal. Psychologists rate it as the number one stressor we will all eventually face. When we say we've "lost" that person, the truth is *we're* lost. The world as we've known it no longer exists. Standing in the ruins of the life we once knew, our disorientation and anguish are often so great, we wonder whether life is worth living.

Being lost, we need a map, a guide, some signpost. The right questions can be a trail in the wilderness that leads us out of the darkness into the light, toward home, healing and eventual wholeness.

"You don't want a million answers
as much as you want a few forever questions."
— Richard Bach

Paradoxically, asking the *right* questions is often the answer to many of life's greatest challenges. Loss and grief ask many questions: *Why me? How could this have happened? How can I stand this pain? How long will I feel like this? Will I ever feel "normal" again? Did I love enough? What if? I should've?...could've?...would've?* And on and on....

When we lose a loved one, we find ourselves asking questions we've never asked before. And it's in those questions that we must dwell. Posing the right questions helps us move through our grief. Answering those questions is essential to our healing.

"Live your questions now, and perhaps even without knowing it, you will live along some distant day into your answers."

— Rainer Maria Rilke

When you think of a *quest*, you probably think of the *Knights of the Round Table*. Today, instead of slaying dragons, we pose and answer questions. The excruciating grief of losing a loved one is like a dragon that threatens to turn our love into a "poison pill." The quest to slay that dragon requires identifying those questions buried in our hearts and pursuing the answers with all our courage. Such a quest is no less demanding, no less heroic, and no less transformative than any knight's quest ever was.

One of the things that helped me in my *Grief Quest* was keeping a journal in which I expressed my pain, my love, past memories and present misery. In my memoir, ***JOYride: How My Late Wife Loved Me Back To Life***, I wrote:

They talk about the fog of war. There's also a fog of grief. I began to compulsively jot down thoughts so as not to forget.

In the weeks preceding Joy's death, I saw myself tied to railroad tracks as an oncoming train bore down on me. As it turned out, the metaphor of a train wreck wasn't accurate. A more apt metaphor was a flood, a tsunami that washed everything away. Tossed on turbulent seas of sorrow, I'm wracked by relentless waves of grief.

Like a captain's log, I recorded the rocky coastline, the pounding surf and the dangerous currents of my new uncharted journey on the Sea of Sorrow. Journaling was an instinctive effort to grab and burn as many memories into my psyche as possible. Above all, to not let Joy go. Journaling was a way to still BE with her!

Your *Grief Quest* means putting your answers into words, no matter how simple or inarticulate. Remember, there are no "right" answers. Pursuing these questions, painful though some may be, will lead you to the depths of your soul where the alchemy of healing takes place.

Not only did Joy ask me that first question—*Was our love a poison pill?*—which propelled me on my *Grief Quest*, she also inspired this workbook in another way. Having lost her first two children, Joy was intimate with loss and grief. It had transformed her into a spiritual teacher who often used the power of questions to help people get to know themselves. If you embark on this *Grief Quest*, you'll get to know yourself and your relationship with your loved one on a deeper level than you thought possible.

"There are years that ask questions and years that answer."
– Zora Neale Hurston

"He explained to me with great insistence that every question possessed a power that did not lie in the answer."
– Elie Wiesel

How Grief Quest Works?

The *Grief Quest* workbook can help guide you along your grief journey in a number of ways. First, it functions as an antidote to the "poison pill" of grief. Just embarking on your *Grief Quest* takes courage and demonstrates your intention to become better, not bitter. It took courage to love. It will take even more courage to live in the face of loss and eventually heal.

Grief Quest utilizes a unique 4-step L.O.V.E. process—

Step 1: Remember the <u>Love</u> and <u>Life</u> you shared.

Journaling had become for me a way to balance the pain-grief connection to Joy with a love connection by reliving our life and love together. At my bereavement group, I shared how I'd been remembering and writing about falling in love with Joy. Our facilitator suggested we all take turns sharing how we fell in love. It was miraculous to witness ravaged faces and grief-stricken hearts suddenly transform as they remembered the joys of their love.

One of the oldest myths of mankind teaches that *remembering* is one of the keys to healing grief. In ancient Egypt, the land of pharaohs and pyramids, perhaps the oldest civilization on Earth, one of their core myths illustrates this truth about grieving.

Isis, the great goddess of Egypt, might well be called the *Goddess of Grief*. When her lover, the god Osiris was murdered and his body torn apart, dismembered into pieces and scattered throughout Egypt, a grief-stricken Isis wandered the land until she found all his body parts and magically put him back together.

One of the greatest myths of antiquity celebrates the magical way Isis grieved. By re-*membering* her dis-membered loved one, she brought him back to life. By re-*membering* the scattered parts of him, she not only made him whole again, she made herself whole.

The death of a loved one is truly a dis-memberment. But it's the bereaved who has been dismembered, feeling "lost," "shattered" and "in pieces." The ancient myth of Isis and Osiris teaches us that in the face of the dismemberment of death, the act of re-*membering* your loved one creates healing and wholeness.

Remembering everything you can about your loved one is a way to balance the pain-grief connection by reliving the love, life and relationship you shared. The questions in *Grief Quest* will help you memorialize your loved one which in itself is healing. The simple act of recording your memories is a tribute to your loved one and all that you shared.

"If I am to wear this mourning cloak, let it be made of the fabric of love, woven by the fine thread of memory."
— Molly Fumia

"Let the joy of your loved one's life begin to take the place of the hurt and anger of the death."
— Darcie D. Sims

STEP 2: <u>OPEN</u> TO YOUR FEELINGS OF GRIEF & EXPRESS THEM.

Our emotions are meant to flow—like a stream, like a river, even like a waterfall—depending upon the depth of our sorrow. Even the word for feelings—"emotion"—contains the word "motion." When painful emotions aren't expressed, they become frozen or crystallized in our body. If they're trapped inside us, they fester, pollute and turn into a poisonous swamp, which can result in illness.

"What soap is for the body, tears are for the soul."
— Jewish Proverb

One of the reasons crying makes us feel better is that tears remove toxins from the body (like the stress hormone cortisol) that build up during times of loss and grief. Tears are the body's natural therapy and medicine.

"Tears are the silent language of grief."
— Voltaire

The magical power of tears was known even in Genesis. According to this biblical commentary, the healing power of tears derives from the Garden of Eden and the creation of *The First Tear....*

"After Adam and Eve were banished from the Garden of Eden, God said to them, 'Now you are about to enter into a world of sorrow and trouble the likes of which staggers the imagination. However, I want you to know that My benevolence and My love for you will never end. I know that you will meet with a lot of tribulation in the world, and that it will embitter your lives. For that reason I give you, out of My heavenly treasure, this priceless pearl, a tear. When grief overtakes you and your heart aches so that you are not able to endure it, and great anguish grips your soul, then there will fall from your eyes this tiny tear and your burden will grow lighter.'"

—unattributed Midrash

Like tears, your emotions need to flow and move through you. It is important to express what you are feeling, not what you "should" be feeling. Don't be kind. Don't be spiritual. Tell the truth about how you are feeling in the moment and release it. The truth will set you free.

Aurora Winter, the author of *From Heartbreak to Happiness*, explains it this way. "Unexpressed feelings are like food poisoning. If you stuff your feelings, you get to keep them. Imagine two people who go out for dinner and both get food poisoning. One of them throws up...and lives. The other 'stuffs it'...and dies. It is absolutely essential that you get whatever is bothering you out of your system."

Expressing your feelings in this workbook is an act of de-toxifying your emotional body. It is a necessary step in your quest to heal your grief.

GRATITUDE *RX*

"Gratitude is not only the greatest of virtues,
but the parent of all the others"
– Cicero

Steps 3 and 4 of your *Grief Quest* are the most difficult and counter-intuitive in the midst of your pain because the questions they ask require you to express gratitude, the emotion furthest from grief. Paradoxically, gratitude is one of the most effective remedies for grief, but it's also the hardest to attain.

What's there to be grateful for?

One of the biggest questions Loss poses is: *What can I be grateful for when I'm in such pain?* The answer is that now, more than ever, you must attempt to appreciate whatever you can. Slaying a dragon might be easier in comparison.

On the scale of emotions, grief is a very low vibration. Gratitude, on the other hand, is a high vibration. The remedy of *GratitudeRx* is essential because it's the antidote to the potential "poison pill" grief can become.

You're probably wondering, *What on earth can I be grateful for when my life has been destroyed by the loss of my loved one?*

You can begin by feeling gratitude for the wonderful gifts that you received during the time you had together. You honor your loved one by expressing gratitude for the life and love you shared.

Alright, you may be saying to yourself, *I may be able to find gratitude for the life and love we shared, but how on earth can I be grateful for my life as it is right now in this terrible moment of loss?*

In a time of such devastating loss, it is essential to make the difficult, courageous and truly heroic effort to be grateful for what you still have in your life. The profound loss you feel needs to be balanced by even a glimmer of gratitude for the life, love, friends, family, work, health, food and shelter you still possess!

In the wake of loss, your life is like a flame that has nearly been extinguished. You need to fan any spark that remains, blow on it with all your might, re-light and ignite that flame. The practice of gratitude will help you do this.

> *"As long as I can I will look at this world for the both of us.*
> *As long as I can I will laugh with the birds,*
> *I will sing with the flowers,*
> *I will pray to the stars,*
> *For the both of us."*
> — Author Unknown

Perhaps another way to think about being grateful for the life you still have is this: your loved one is no longer able to take a breath of air, feel life pulsing through them, bask in the warmth of the sun, sleep, dream, eat, listen to bird song and music, have a conversation, laugh, walk, dance, run, joke, get angry, be frustrated—*LIVE!*

You honor your loved one's life by appreciating all the ways in which you are still alive and all you still have in this world. It's a difficult, truly heroic quest to hunt in your darkness for the faintest flicker of gratitude, sift through the rubble of your life for anything you can be grateful for, dumpster dive through the garbage of your grief for any crumbs of nourishing gratefulness, pan in the mud of your despair for any speck of the gold of gratitude that you can still find in your life. The *Grief Quest* is not for the faint of heart. But such a noble and heroic quest honors your loved one and your love.

> *"Keep your heart in wonder*
> *at the daily miracles of your life."*
> –Kahlil Gibran

In 1999, Dr. Masaru Emoto published his ground-breaking study "Messages from Water," which discovered that water reacts to our words and thoughts. His experiments used powerful electron microscopes to capture newly formed crystals in frozen water samples. According to Dr. Emoto, thoughts, prayers, music and meditation transmit positive vibrations to water that affect the way it crystallizes. Water exposed to loving words showed brilliant, complex, and beautiful crystals. In contrast, water exposed to negative thoughts or words formed incomplete, asymmetrical, ugly crystals.

Dr. Emoto stated that the most beautiful water crystals were formed when they were exposed to the words or emotion of *Love* and *Thanks*. When asked what emotion had the most powerful effect on water, even purifying polluted waters, he answered, "Gratitude."

Mother and daughter grief experts, Drs. Gloria & Heidi Horsley, have conducted extensive research in the field of loss and bereavement, and have found that many scientific studies conclude that cultivating gratitude leads to the biggest increase in feelings of well-being. So much so, that in their *8 Steps to Hope* bereavement program, Step #1 is "Find Gratitude."

STEP 3: <u>VALUE</u> (BY APPRECIATING AND ACKNOWLEDGING WITH GRATITUDE) THE MANY GIFTS YOUR LOVED ONE HAS GIVEN YOU.

There are countless things to be grateful for about your loved one's presence in your life. Don't forget all the gifts of their *presence* because you're so focused on their *absence*. Another way to *re-member* your loved one is to appreciate and acknowledge the gifts and opportunities they brought you. *What did your love teach you? How did your relationship expand you? What new things did you experience because of your loved one?* As the old song goes, "Because of you...."

There may be times when you remember an unpleasant situation that comes with any relationship and that can trigger remorse, regret and guilt. But that, too, is part of the remembering...and valuing even those situations for what they taught you.

"Blessed is the influence of one true, loving human soul on another."
— *George Elliot*

"The giving of love is an education in itself."
— *Eleanor Roosevelt*

STEP 4: <u>EMBRACE</u> YOUR LIFE
BY SEARCHING FOR ANY SHRED OF GRATITUDE
& PANNING FOR THE GOLD THAT STILL EXISTS.

This step is the equivalent of keeping a gratitude journal. Typically, it's suggested you write five things you're grateful for that day. In the midst of grief, three things will do. Review the day and include anything, however small, that could be a source of gratitude that day.

It could be as mundane as getting a decent night's sleep or as momentous as finally resolving some conflict. Amazing things—like a rainbow, a flower in bloom, a butterfly. Or simple things—like a great cup of coffee, no traffic, finding a parking space. You can be thankful for things in general, like your home, your health, your family, your friends. You can also write about something you're thankful for about yourself, for example, "I'm thankful for my hands that helped me do so many things today" or " I'm thankful for my eyesight so that I'm independent and can see the blue sky through the break in the clouds."

Practice looking for what there is to appreciate in every situation, even in negative situations. There may be times when you have a particularly frustrating experience, for example, with customer service. Then you can be grateful for the opportunity to exercise your patience or even your anger.

It's especially important on bad days to express gratitude because that's when you need it the most. On bad days you'll find it hard to find things to be grateful for, but no matter how bad, you can be grateful for just breathing, for the sun shining, for having food and shelter and not being in excruciating physical pain! Just having a decent bed to get into at night is something to be grateful for, or even that the day is finally over. And, if you can't think of anything, you can be grateful that you showed up on this *Grief Quest* to do this workbook one more day.

Try not to repeat your gratitudes. The more creative you are, the more you're exercising your gratitude muscle, and the more effective the Gratitude*Rx* will be. By training yourself to look for things to be grateful for each day, you begin developing the habit of focusing on what you *have* rather than what you've lost. This seems impossible, but ultimately you will be training yourself to focus on the blessing that your loved one has been for you, rather than the suffering of your loss.

"Can you see the holiness in those things you take for granted—a paved road or a washing machine? If you concentrate on finding what is good in every situation, you will discover that your life will suddenly be filled with gratitude, a feeling that nurtures the soul."
—Rabbi Harold Kushner

"Let us rise up and be thankful, for if we didn't learn a lot today, at least we learned a little, and if we didn't learn a little, at least we didn't get sick, and if we got sick, at least we didn't die; so, let us all be thankful.
—Buddha

L. O. V. E.

Let's review the 4-Step L.O.V.E. process:

1. L — Remember the LOVE and relationship you shared.

2. O — OPEN to your feelings of grief and express them.

3. V — VALUE and Appreciate the many gifts your loved one has given you.

4. E — EMBRACE your life by searching for the slightest shred of gratitude and panning for the gold that still exists.

L——Love your memories

O——Open to your grief

V——Value the gifts

E——Embrace your life

When You Lose A Loved One
(You Lose a Part of You)

It's Time to
FIND YOURSELF

When you lose a loved one and your life is devastated by grief, you often feel as though you've lost a part of yourself. You begin to confront some of the big questions that Loss invariably poses about life, love, death, meaning, purpose, etc. In the agony of loss and grief, you begin to wonder who you are and ask questions you've never asked before. It's in those questions that you find new parts of yourself. Another aspect of your *Grief Quest*, when you've lost someone you love, is finding more of who you are. When you lose a loved one, it's time to find yourself!

Every seventh day of your *Grief Quest* there's a day of rest, a kind of sabbath, in which the focus of the questions shifts to you and *Finding Yourself.*

"But before I look out...let me first of all gaze within myself."
— Rainier Maria Rilke

"Not until we are lost do we begin to understand ourselves."
— Henry David Thoreau

DIRECTIONS

- Every day you'll be asked four L.O.V.E. questions to help you remember your love, express your grief, value the gifts and embrace your life.

- Spend at least 5 minutes a day pondering and answering these questions. There are blank L.O.V.E. Notes pages at the back of the workbook if you need them.

- On the seventh day, you'll take a break and explore another aspect of the *Grief Quest*—Finding Yourself. You'll be asked four questions that will help you discover more of who you are and who you are becoming.

- Repeat for at least 4 cycles or 28 days.

OTHER PEOPLE'S *GRIEF QUESTS*

Here's what other bereaved people have said about their *Grief Quest*:

- *Writing in the workbook each day has allowed me to access specific memories, feelings and events that brought up much sadness, yet allowed me to cry and express my feelings freely. I looked forward each morning to doing the process, knowing that it would trigger my grief, yet wanting and relishing that experience. It helped create a container, a time for my grief, that was sacred.*

- *I loved the inspirational stories and quotes interspersed throughout the workbook.*

- *The fact that it was repetitive created a ritual which became more and more powerful as I did it.*

- *The L Questions for memories were the easiest. The E Questions (Embrace your life) were the most difficult and required the most creativity. But it was worth it.*

- *Grief Quest is like a bridge for grievers and holds the space for their healing.*

- *The workbook empowered me with choices about how to process my grief in a way that was truly healing by questioning and journaling.*

- *I can only speak for myself, but Grief Quest works and should be a valuable tool for anyone going through grief.*

BITTER OR BETTER?

I was inspired to write *Grief Quest: A Workbook & Journal to Heal the Grieving Heart* because of my extraordinary experience of love and loss, and the guidance I was blessed to receive from my late wife, Joy.

If you use this workbook to embark on your own *Grief Quest*, you are intending to heal so that your love doesn't become a "poison pill." That's the challenge we face when we lose someone we love.

Life eventually grinds us all down. It's our attitude towards the millstone of losses we inevitably suffer that determines whether we're ground to dust or polished into a diamond. It's simple—you'll either get bitter or better. But it's largely an attitude, a habit of mind, which is all we can really control.

Grief Quest is an *Rx* for the emotional heart attack of losing a loved one and the soul sickness of grief. Science has demonstrated that it takes 21 to 28 days to create a new habit. Go on the *Grief Quest* for 28 days, and see if you don't experience a positive shift in the way you feel. Consider *Grief Quest* your personal rehab and, like any training or workout, the more you put into it, the more you'll get out of it.

Though I've gone through my own losses, I can't imagine yours, except to know that it is one of the most difficult things you've ever faced. I hope this workbook helps you on your journey.

— I. J. Weinstock, 2012

DEDICATION

I dedicate my *Grief Quest* to

The grace + love of God our father + to
Jesus Christ my Lord and Savior

21

Because of the hope I have in them I know I
will be reunited with my precious Derek, Dad, Friends + Family

I remember when we first...

_____

_____

_____

_____

_____

_____

_____

_____

"Death leaves a heartache no one can heal,
love leaves a memory no one can steal."
— From a headstone in Ireland

My grief makes me feeI...

_____

_____

_____

_____

_____

_____

_____

Here are 10 things I loved about loving you:

_____

_____

_____

_____

_____

_____

_____

_____

_____

"If the only prayer you said in your whole life was "thank you,"
that would suffice." — Meister Eckhart

Despite my loss and grief, I'm grateful for these
three things still in my life:

_____

_____

_____

_____

_____

_____

_____

_____

L *Remembering how you _____ makes me laugh.*

_____

_____

_____

_____

_____

_____

_____

_____

"We are healed of a suffering only by expressing it to the full."
— Marcel Proust

Since my loss I can't ...

_____

_____

_____

_____

_____

_____

_____

_____

Having you in my life gave me
a whole new perspective on...

_____

_____

_____

_____

_____

_____

_____

"Gratitude is an art of painting an adversity into a lovely picture."
— Kak Sri

Despite my grief, I'm grateful for my family or friends who ...

_____

_____

_____

_____

_____

_____

_____

L

I remember when you used to say to me...

_____

_____

_____

_____

_____

_____

_____

_____

O

"Every sinking into despair has within it an energy
to move us higher." — Dr. Wayne Dyer

I become angry when I think...

_____

_____

_____

_____

_____

_____

_____

*I'm so grateful for the love we shared
because it gave me the opportunity to...*

_____

_____

_____

_____

_____

_____

_____

_____

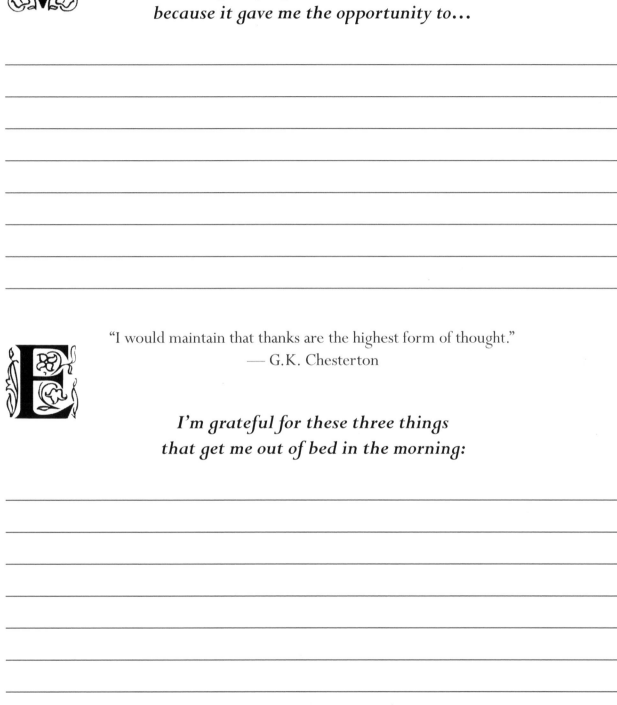

"I would maintain that thanks are the highest form of thought."
— G.K. Chesterton

*I'm grateful for these three things
that get me out of bed in the morning:*

_____

_____

_____

_____

_____

_____

_____

L

I loved it when we...

_____

_____

_____

_____

_____

_____

_____

"Give sorrow words: the grief that does not speak
whispers the o'er fraught heart and bids it break." —Shakespeare

O

Without you I feel...

_____

_____

_____

_____

_____

_____

_____

_____

I find myself saying or doing _____
just like you used to.

_____

_____

_____

_____

_____

_____

_____

"The unthankful heart… discovers no mercies;
but let the thankful heart sweep through the day and,
as the magnet finds the iron, so it will find, in every hour,
some heavenly blessings!" — Henry Ward Beecher

I'm grateful for these things that get me out the door each day:

_____

_____

_____

_____

_____

L

My favorite photos of you remind me of...

_____

_____

_____

_____

_____

_____

_____

_____

"Sorrow makes us all children again — destroys all differences of intellect.
The wisest know nothing." —— Ralph Waldo Emerson

O

I'm tired and exhausted—everything is...

_____

_____

_____

_____

_____

_____

_____

_____

_____

I would never have learned about _____
if you hadn't been in my life.

_____

_____

_____

_____

_____

_____

"We can only be said to be alive in those moments when our hearts
are conscious of our treasures."—Thornton Wilder

Despite my grief, I'm grateful for these three things
to appreciate in Nature:

_____

_____

_____

_____

_____

_____

_____

_____

_____

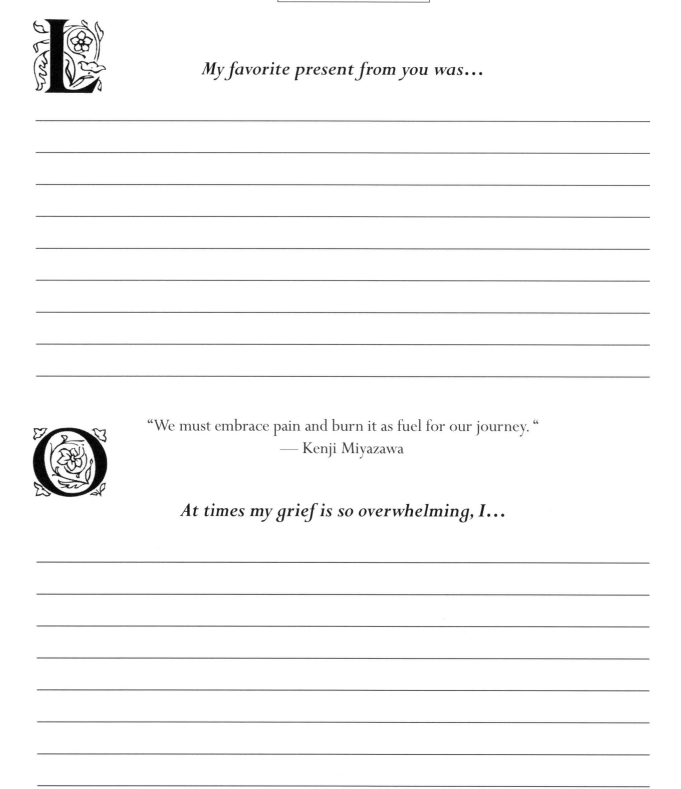

My favorite present from you was...

_____

_____

_____

_____

_____

_____

_____

_____

"We must embrace pain and burn it as fuel for our journey. "
— Kenji Miyazawa

At times my grief is so overwhelming, I...

_____

_____

_____

_____

_____

_____

_____

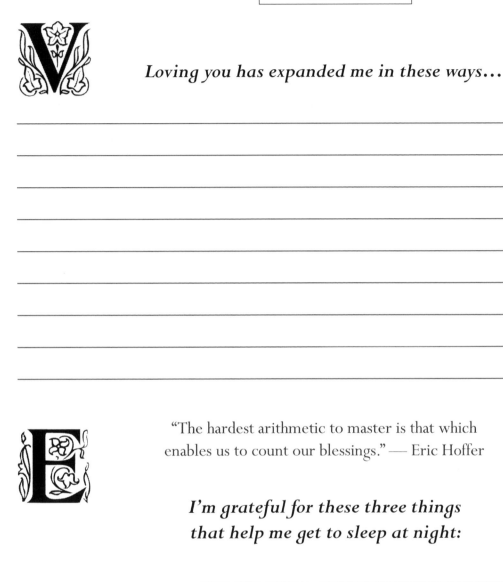

Loving you has expanded me in these ways...

_____

_____

_____

_____

_____

_____

_____

_____

"The hardest arithmetic to master is that which
enables us to count our blessings." — Eric Hoffer

*I'm grateful for these three things
that help me get to sleep at night:*

_____

_____

_____

_____

_____

_____

_____

_____

IND YOURSELF

Before your loss, what were your three greatest passions?

_____

_____

_____

_____

_____

_____

_____

"When you lose a loved one, it's time to find yourself!"
— I. J. Weinstock

What place that you have never been
would you like most to visit?

_____

_____

_____

_____

_____

_____

_____

34

IND YOURSELF

What is your favorite form of relaxation? Recreation?

_____

_____

_____

_____

_____

_____

_____

"Truly, it is in the darkness that one finds the light. So when we are in sorrow,
then this light is nearest of all to us." — Meister Eckhart

What's your greatest talent?
What talent do you have that you're not using?

_____

_____

_____

_____

_____

_____

There's no disaster that can't become a blessing,
and no blessing that can't become a disaster

— Richard Bach

THE OLD MAN AND HIS HORSE

Once there was an old man who lived in a small village. Although poor, he was envied by all for he owned a beautiful white horse. Even the king coveted his treasure. A horse like this had never been seen before – such was its splendor, its majesty, its strength.

People offered fabulous prices for the steed, but the old man always refused. "This horse is not a horse to me," he would tell them. "It is a person. How could you sell a person? He is a friend, not a possession. How could you sell a friend." Though the man was poor, he never sold the horse.

One morning he found that the horse was not in his stable. All the village came to mock him. "You old fool," they scoffed, "we told you that someone would steal your horse. You are so poor. How could you ever protect such a valuable animal? You should have sold him. You could have gotten whatever price you wanted. You would have been rich. Now the horse is gone and you've been cursed with misfortune."

The old man responded, "Don't judge too quickly. Say only that the horse is not in the stable. That is all we know. If I've been cursed or not, how can you know? How can you judge?"

The people argued, "Don't make us out to be fools! We may not be philosophers, but the simple fact that your horse is gone is a curse."

The old man spoke again. "All I know is that the stable is empty and the horse is gone. Whether it's a curse or a blessing, I can't say. Who can say what will come next?"

The people of the village laughed. They had always thought the old man was a fool; if he wasn't, he would have sold the horse and lived off the money. But instead, he was living hand to mouth in the misery of poverty. Where before they thought him a fool, now they were convinced he was crazy.

After fifteen days, the horse returned. He hadn't been stolen; he had run away into the forest. Not only had he returned, he had brought a dozen wild horses with him. Once again, the village people gathered around the woodcutter and spoke. "Old man, you were right and we were wrong. What we thought was a curse was a blessing. Please forgive us."

The man responded, "Once again, you go too far. Say only that the horse is back and that a dozen horses returned with him, but don't judge. How do you know if this is a blessing or not? You see only a fragment. Unless you know the whole story, how can you judge? You read only one page of a book. Can you judge the whole book? Life is so vast. Don't say that this is a blessing. No one knows."

"Maybe the old man is right," the villagers said to one another. So they said little. But down deep, they knew he was wrong. They knew it was a blessing. Twelve wild horses had returned. With a little work, the animals could be broken and trained and sold for much money.

The old man had a son, an only son. The young man began to break the wild horses. After a few days, he fell from one of the horses and broke both legs. Once again the villagers gathered around the old man.

"You were right," they said. "The dozen horses were not a blessing. They were a curse. Your only son has broken both his legs, and now in your old age you have no one to help you. Now you are poorer than ever."

The old man spoke again. "Say only that my son broke his legs. Who knows if it is a blessing or a curse? No one knows."

It so happened that a few weeks later war was declared. All the young men of the village were required to join the army. Only the son of the old man was excluded, because he was injured. Once again the people gathered around the old man, crying and screaming because their sons had been taken. There was little chance they would return because the enemy was strong and the war would be lost. They would never see their sons again.

"You were right, old man," They wept. "Your son's accident was a blessing. His legs may be broken, but at least he is with you. Our sons are gone forever."

The old man spoke again. "Say only this. Your sons had to go to war, and mine did not. No one knows if it is a blessing or a curse. No one is wise enough to know. Only God knows."

— *Chinese Parable*

❖　　❖　　❖

L

You were special in so many ways...

_____

_____

_____

_____

_____

_____

_____

"Tears have a wisdom all their own. They come when a person has relaxed enough
to let go and to work through their sorrow. They are the natural bleeding
of an emotional wound, carrying the poison out of the system.
Here lies the road to recovery."
— F. Alexander Magoun

O

There are times when I can't stop crying and I feel...
And there are other times I can't cry and I feel...

_____

_____

_____

_____

_____

_____

_____

*You showed me how to play, and
I'm going to _____ in your honor.*

_____

_____

_____

_____

_____

_____

_____

"We often take for granted the very things
that most deserve our gratitude." — Cynthia Ozick

*Despite my sorrow, I'm grateful for these
three things of beauty in my life:*

_____

_____

_____

_____

_____

_____

What amazed me most about you was...

_____

_____

_____

_____

_____

_____

_____

"It's so curious: one can resist tears and 'behave' very well in the hardest hours of grief.
But then someone makes you a friendly sign behind a window, or one notices
that a flower that was in bud only yesterday has suddenly blossomed, or a letter
slips from a drawer... and everything collapses." — Colette

Sleep is difficult now because...

_____

_____

_____

_____

_____

_____

_____

_____

My priorities have changed since losing you.
What's important to me now is...

_____

_____

_____

_____

_____

_____

_____

_____

"Gratitude is the fairest blossom which springs from the soul."
—— Henry Ward Beecher

Despite my loss, I'm grateful for these
three things that help lift my spirit:

_____

_____

_____

_____

_____

_____

_____

_____

L

I loved watching you...

_____

_____

_____

_____

_____

_____

_____

"The sorrow which has no vent in tears may make other organs weep."
—— Henry Maudsley

O

Since my loss I can't make decisions because...
The decisions that have been hardest for me are...

_____

_____

_____

_____

_____

_____

_____

Loving you has made me a better person in these ways:

_____

_____

_____

_____

_____

_____

_____

"Most human beings have an almost infinite capacity
for taking things for granted." — Aldous Huxley

*Today I'm grateful for these three things
I hadn't noticed before:*

_____

_____

_____

_____

_____

_____

_____

_____

L

I remember how _____ always made us laugh.

_____

_____

_____

_____

_____

_____

_____

_____

_____

"While grief is fresh, every attempt to divert only irritates."
— James Boswell

O

Sometimes I feel so bad I want to hide from the world.
People don't understand—they...

_____

_____

_____

_____

_____

_____

_____

_____

You took care of me so well, and in your memory
I'm going to take care of myself by...

_____

_____

_____

_____

_____

_____

_____

"At times our own light goes out and is rekindled by a spark from another person.
Each of us has cause to think with deep gratitude of those who have
lighted the flame within us." — Albert Schweitzer

I'm grateful for all the help I've been given and the love
I've been shown during this terrible ordeal, such as:

_____

_____

_____

_____

_____

_____

L   *I was so proud of you when...*

_____

_____

_____

_____

_____

_____

_____

_____

"The mind is its own place, and in itself,
can make heaven of Hell and a hell of Heaven." — John Milton

O   *I feel lousy! If you were here you'd say or do* _____
and it would make me feel better.

_____

_____

_____

_____

_____

_____

_____

_____

_____

Losing you has taught me
_____ about life.

_____

_____

_____

_____

_____

_____

_____

_____

"You can clutch the past so tightly to your chest that it leaves your arms too full to embrace the present." — Jan Glidewell

I'm grateful for these three distractions that
have helped me cope with my grief:

_____

_____

_____

_____

_____

_____

_____

*If I were creating a "highlight reel" of your life,
it would include...*

_____

_____

_____

_____

_____

_____

_____

_____

_____

"No one ever told me that grief felt so like fear."
— C.S. Lewis

Since losing you, I'm anxious, worried, afraid of...

_____

_____

_____

_____

_____

_____

_____

_____

V

You introduced me to so many new experiences, such as:

_____

_____

_____

_____

_____

_____

_____

_____

_____

E

*"Let us not look back in anger or forward in fear,
but around in awareness."— James Thurber*

**Despite my grief, I'm grateful for these little things
that make life worth living:**

_____

_____

_____

_____

_____

_____

_____

_____

IND YOURSELF

What do you want to learn more about?

_____

_____

_____

_____

_____

_____

"The heart that breaks open can contain the whole universe."
— Joanna Macy

In the past, what were your dreams?
What blocked you from realizing them?

_____

_____

_____

_____

_____

_____

_____

IND YOURSELF

What brings you peace?

_____

_____

_____

_____

_____

_____

"There is an alchemy in sorrow. It can be transmuted into wisdom,
which, if it does not bring joy, can yet bring happiness." — Pearl S. Buck

What was the craziest thing you ever did?

_____

_____

_____

_____

_____

_____

_____

_____

Tears are shed when we are born and they usher us out when we die: the meaning of life is a dance in between.

– Mitch Carmody

PARABLE OF THE TWINS

Once upon a time, twin boys were conceived in the same womb. Weeks passed, and the twins developed. As their awareness grew, they laughed for joy—"Isn't it great that we were conceived? Isn't it great to be alive?

Together, the twins explored their world. When they found their mother's cord that gave them life, they sang for joy—"How great is our mother's love, that she shares her own life with us!"

As weeks stretched into months, the twins noticed how much each was changing. "What does it mean?" asked the one.

"It means that our stay in this world is drawing to an end," said the other.

"But I don't want to go," said the one, "I want to stay here always."

"We have no choice," said the other. "But maybe there is life after birth!"

"But how can there be?" responded the one. "We will shed our life cord, and how is life possible without it? Besides, we have seen no evidence that others were here before us, and none of them have returned to tell us that there is a life after birth. No, this is the end."

And so the one fell into deep despair, saying, "If conception ends in birth, what is the purpose of life in the womb? It's meaningless! Maybe there is no mother after all?"

"But there has to be," protested the other. "How else did we get here? How do we remain alive?"

"Have you ever seen our mother?" said the one. "Maybe she lives only in our minds. Maybe we made her up because the idea made us feel good?"

And so the last days in the womb were filled with deep questioning and fear. Finally, the moment of birth arrived.

When the twins had passed from their world, they opened their eyes. They cried. For what they saw exceeded their fondest dreams.

❖   ❖   ❖

Life is eternal; and love is immortal; and death is only a horizon;
and a horizon is nothing save the limit of our sight.

—Rossiter W. Raymond

JOY AND SORROW

Then a woman said, "Speak to us of Joy and Sorrow."
And he answered: Your joy is your sorrow unmasked.
And the selfsame well from which your laughter rises
was oftentimes filled with your tears.
And how else can it be?

The deeper that sorrow carves into your being,
the more joy you can contain.
Is not the cup that holds your wine
the very cup that was burned in the potter's oven?
And is not the lute that soothes your spirit,
the very wood that was hollowed with knives?

When you are joyous,
look deep into your heart and you shall find
it is only that which has given you sorrow
that is giving you joy.

When you are sorrowful, look again in your heart,
and you shall see that in truth you are weeping
for that which has been your delight.

Some of you say, "Joy is greater than sorrow,"
and others say, "Nay, sorrow is the greater."
But I say unto you, they are inseparable.

–Khalil Gibran

These are some of the things
I want to tell the world about you:

_____

_____

_____

_____

_____

_____

_____

"To experience and embrace the pain of loss is just as much a part of life
as to experience the joy of love." — Alan Wolfelt

Deciding what to do with your things makes me feel...

_____

_____

_____

_____

_____

_____

_____

_____

_____

V   *I've become more aware of _____ because of you.*

_____

_____

_____

_____

_____

_____

"I loved the boy with the utmost love of which my soul is capable of and he is taken from me
—yet in the agony of my spirit in surrendering such a treasure, I feel a thousand times richer
than if I had never possessed it."— William Wordsworth

E   *Despite my grief, I'm grateful for these little things*
that make life worth living:

_____

_____

_____

_____

_____

_____

_____

_____

L

I remember how you loved to...

_____

_____

_____

_____

_____

_____

_____

"Tears won't bring him back, but they might bring *you* back."
— Barbra Streisand in The Prince of Tides

O

*Part of me wants to feel better, but there's another part
that doesn't want to feel better. Why?*

_____

_____

_____

_____

_____

_____

_____

*Having loved you has taught me so much
about myself. I learned that I am...*

_____

_____

_____

_____

_____

_____

_____

"Let us be grateful to people who make us happy;
they are the charming gardeners who make our souls blossom."
—Marcel Proust

*Despite my loss, I'm grateful for the opportunities
for love that I still have in my life, such as:*

_____

_____

_____

_____

_____

_____

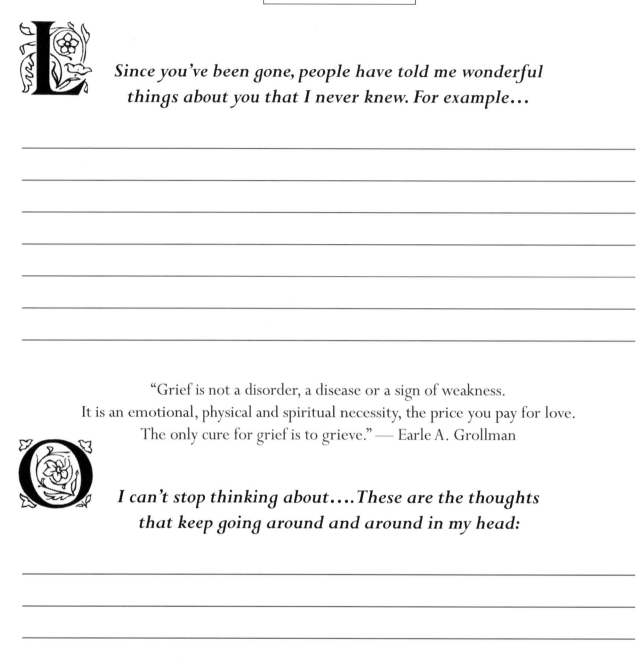

Since you've been gone, people have told me wonderful things about you that I never knew. For example...

_____

_____

_____

_____

_____

_____

"Grief is not a disorder, a disease or a sign of weakness.
It is an emotional, physical and spiritual necessity, the price you pay for love.
The only cure for grief is to grieve." — Earle A. Grollman

I can't stop thinking about....These are the thoughts that keep going around and around in my head:

_____

_____

_____

_____

_____

_____

_____

Losing you has taught me to embrace life more fully.
So before I die, I want to...

_____

_____

_____

_____

_____

_____

_____

"Enjoy the little things, for one day you may look back
and realize they were the big things." — Robert Brault

Today I'm grateful for the opportunity to...

_____

_____

_____

_____

_____

_____

_____

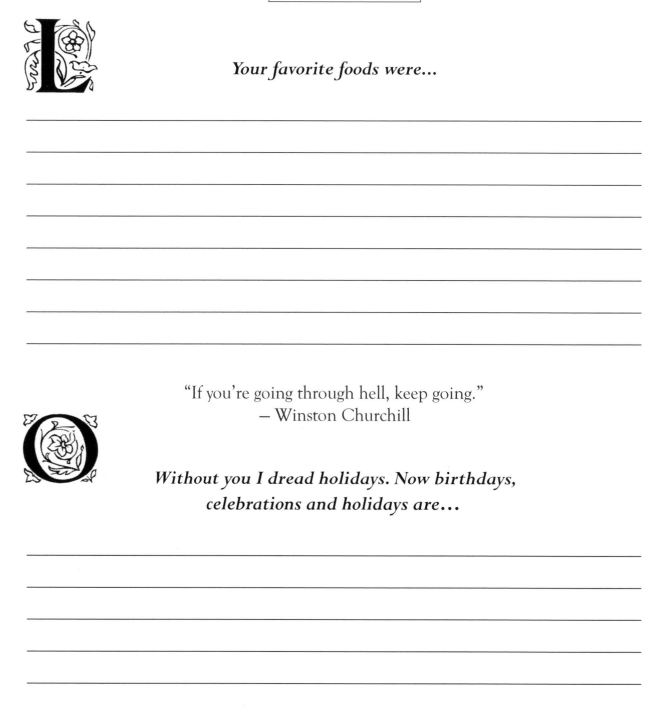

Your favorite foods were...

_____

_____

_____

_____

_____

_____

_____

"If you're going through hell, keep going."
— Winston Churchill

Without you I dread holidays. Now birthdays,
celebrations and holidays are...

_____

_____

_____

_____

_____

_____

_____

_____

V *I'm grateful for all the fun you brought into my life, like:*

_____

_____

_____

_____

_____

_____

_____

"A grateful person trusts enough to give life another chance,
to stay open for surprises." — Brother David Steindal-Rast

E *Today I'm grateful for _____. I'm also going
to start something new to be grateful for, and that is...*

_____

_____

_____

_____

_____

_____

_____

L   *I remember how surprised you were when...*

_____

_____

_____

_____

_____

_____

"My grief and pain are mine. I have earned them. They are a part of me.
Only in feeling them do I open myself to the lessons they can teach."
— Anne Wilson Schaef

O   *I escape my pain by... I comfort myself by...*

_____

_____

_____

_____

_____

_____

_____

I never thanked you enough. Thank you for...

_____

_____

_____

_____

_____

_____

_____

_____

"There is not a more pleasing exercise of the mind than gratitude.
It is accompanied with such an inward satisfaction that the duty
is sufficiently rewarded by the performance." — Joseph Addison

*Today I'm grateful for _____. I'm also grateful
for the opportunity to honor you by...*

_____

_____

_____

_____

_____

_____

_____

You thought it was very funny when…

_____

_____

_____

_____

_____

_____

_____

_____

_____

"If you suppress grief too much, it can well redouble."
— Moliere

Regret is often a part of grief. I regret…

_____

_____

_____

_____

_____

_____

_____

_____

I laugh now at things that I know you would find funny,
like _____. Thank you for helping me smile.

"We have no right to ask when a sorrow comes, 'Why did this happen to me?'
unless we ask the same question for every joy that comes our way."
— Author Unknown

Today I'm grateful for these
three things I hadn't noticed before:

FIND YOURSELF

Name three things that used to excite you?

_____

_____

_____

_____

_____

_____

"Deep unspeakable suffering may well be called a baptism,
a regeneration, the initiation into a new state." — George Eliot

*If you could choose any job or vocation,
what would you most like to do?*

_____

_____

_____

_____

_____

_____

_____

IND YOURSELF

Is there anything you regret not having done so far in your life? If so, what?

_____

_____

_____

_____

_____

_____

_____

"If we had no winter, the spring would not be so pleasant;
if we did not sometimes taste of adversity, prosperity would not be so welcome."
—— Ann Bradstreet

What are you most proud of?

_____

_____

_____

_____

_____

_____

_____

MISSING A PIECE OF ME

Early in my grief journey a woman who'd already crossed this Valley of the Shadow of Death told me that, despite the pain and anguish I felt, I was walking on hallowed ground, and that there was a sacred dimension to grief that I would miss once I'd healed. At the time I didn't understand what she meant. I couldn't imagine missing the agony I felt. I wanted my pain to be over ASAP.

A few years later I came across a wonderful children's book by Shel Silverstein called, *The Missing Piece*, and it reminded me of what that wise woman had said. The story was about a circle that was missing a slice, a wedge. The circle wanted to be whole so it went searching for its missing piece. But because it was incomplete, it could only roll slowly. So slow that it could smell the flowers, converse with beetles and play with butterflies for the very first time.

It rolled far and wide and found lots of pieces, but none of them fit. So it kept searching, rolling and rolling until one day it found a piece that fit perfectly. The circle was so happy. Now it was whole. Nothing was missing.

As a perfect circle, it could roll very fast now, too fast to smell the flowers, chat with the beetles or play with the butterflies. It soon realized how much it had been missing when it was rolling so fast.

I remembered what that wise woman had told me and now appreciated what she was trying to say. Missing a piece of us gives us a brief glimpse into all that we've ordinarily been missing. Grief can, in slowing us down and taking us out of "normal" life, be a sacred albeit painful gift that can teach us how to live more fully.

— I. J. Weinstock

A REASON TO LIVE

There's a story from the Holocaust about a group of Jews who were escaping the Nazis. They were trying to get over a mountain, and they were carrying the sick and the children. At a certain point, the old people couldn't go on. They told the others, "We're a burden. Go on without us."

A younger but wise leader told them, "The mothers need a rest, so instead of just sitting there and dying, would you take the babies and walk as far as you can?"

Incredibly, once the old people held the babies in their arms, they had a reason to live. And they all made it over the mountain and survived.

*Our greatest glory is not in never falling
but in rising every time we fall.*

— Confucius

People would be surprised to know that you...

_____

_____

_____

_____

_____

_____

"We found that our circle of friends had shifted... People we thought were good friends became distant. Casual acquaintances became suddenly close, sustainers of life for us. Grief changes the rules and sometimes rearranges the combinations." — Martha Whitemore Hickman

It makes me mad when people...

_____

_____

_____

_____

_____

_____

_____

_____

Losing you has taught me this about death:

_____

_____

_____

_____

_____

_____

*"When eating bamboo sprouts, remember
the man who planted them."*—— *Chinese Proverb*

*Despite my grief, I'm grateful for these
small things that sustain me and help me survive:*

_____

_____

_____

_____

_____

_____

_____

_____

You always laughed when I...

_____

_____

_____

_____

_____

_____

_____

_____

_____

"Let mourning stop when one's grief is fully expressed."
— Confucius

What I have to say to God about losing you is this...
(You have permission to be angry)

_____

_____

_____

_____

_____

_____

_____

_____

*To honor you, I'm going to do something
I've been afraid to do. I'm going to...*

_____

_____

_____

_____

_____

_____

_____

"When I started counting my blessings
my whole life turned around."— Willie Nelson

*Today I'm grateful for these three tools
that help me cope:*

_____

_____

_____

_____

_____

_____

One of my favorite memories of your birthday was...

_____

_____

_____

_____

_____

_____

"There are things that we don't want to happen but have to accept,
things we don't want to know but have to learn,
and people we can't live without but have to let go."
– Author Unknown

I can't _____ because you're not here.
And it makes me feel...

_____

_____

_____

_____

_____

_____

_____

I know that you would want me to _____.
I'm going to try to do that for you. For me.

_____

_____

_____

_____

_____

_____

"In our daily lives, we must see that it is not happiness that makes us grateful,
but the gratefulness that makes us happy..." — Albert Clarke

Despite my grief, I'm grateful for these
three things that give me hope or faith:

_____

_____

_____

_____

_____

_____

_____

L *We used to love to do these three things together:*

_____

_____

_____

_____

_____

_____

_____

_____

_____

O "To spare oneself from grief at all cost can be achieved only at the price of total detachment, which excludes the ability to experience happiness" — Ralph Waldo Emerson

Every time I see something that reminds me of you, I feel...

_____

_____

_____

_____

_____

_____

_____

_____

*My grief at losing you has connected me to other people
who've lost a loved one in ways I never imagined.
Losing you has broken but also opened my heart, and I feel...*

_____

_____

_____

_____

_____

_____

_____

"The highest tribute to the dead is not grief but gratitude."
——Thornton Wilder

**I'm grateful for the opportunity to honor you
by living more fully in this way:**

_____

_____

_____

_____

_____

_____

_____

_____

L

I'll never forget how you...

_____

_____

_____

_____

_____

_____

_____

_____

O "Your pain is the breaking of the shell that encloses your understanding.
Even as the stone of the fruit must break, that its heart
may stand in the sun, so you must know pain." — Khalil Gibran

*I caught myself laughing for the first time since you're gone.
I'm confused and have mixed feelings because...*

_____

_____

_____

_____

_____

_____

I miss being known the way you knew me. I miss you knowing things no one else knew about me, such as:

> "Some complain that roses have thorns,
> others rejoice that thorns have roses!"
> —— Unknown

**Despite my loss, I'm grateful for these
three things that nurture me:**

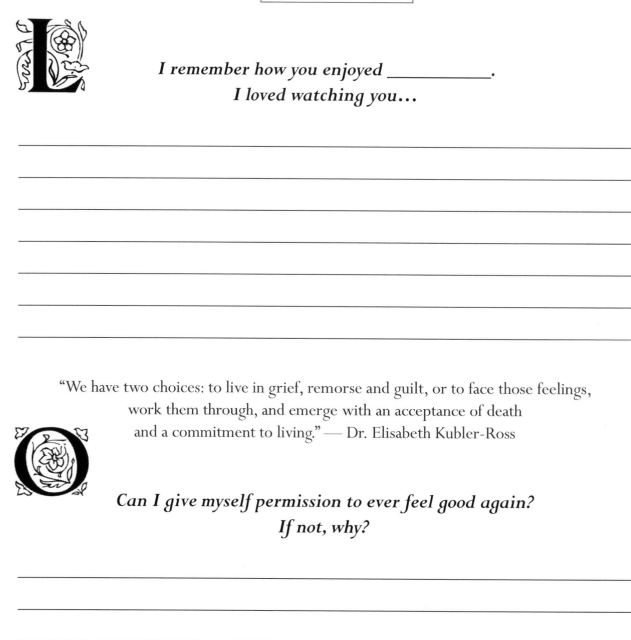

I remember how you enjoyed _____.
I loved watching you...

_____

_____

_____

_____

_____

_____

"We have two choices: to live in grief, remorse and guilt, or to face those feelings, work them through, and emerge with an acceptance of death and a commitment to living." — Dr. Elisabeth Kubler-Ross

Can I give myself permission to ever feel good again?
If not, why?

_____

_____

_____

_____

_____

_____

*Here are some of the "gifts" that knowing
and loving you has given me:*

_____

_____

_____

_____

_____

_____

_____

_____

"Look not mournfully into the past, it comes not back again.
Wisely improve the present, it is thine."
— Henry Wadsworth Longfellow

*Being grateful these days is so hard, yet I am thankful
for these blessings that are still in my life:*

_____

_____

_____

_____

_____

_____

FIND YOURSELF

When in your life have you felt most passionate and alive?

_____

_____

_____

_____

_____

_____

"If there is meaning in life at all, then there must be a meaning in suffering."
—Victor Frankl

Prior to losing your loved one, what was the most difficult challenge
in your life? What did you learn from it?

_____

_____

_____

_____

_____

_____

_____

FIND YOURSELF

What's one of the nicest things you've ever done for someone?
What's one of the nicest things someone has ever done for you?
And what's the nicest thing you've done for yourself?

_____

_____

_____

_____

_____

_____

"A wounded deer leaps the highest." — Emily Dickenson

Aside from your relationship, what have been your
three most meaningful experiences?

The loss of a loved one confronts us with our own mortality in a way nothing else can. We're forced to think about death. And whether there is anything beyond our day-to-day lives. If we are ever to be receptive to messages from beyond the veil and communication with the Afterlife, it is when we have lost a loved one.

— I. J. Weinstock

THE WATERBUG & THE DRAGONFLY

Below the surface of a quiet pond lived a little colony of waterbugs. They were a happy colony, living far away from the sun. For many months they were very busy, scurrying over the soft mud on the bottom of the pond. They did not notice that every once in a while one of their colony seemed to lose interest in going about with its friends. Clinging to the stem of a pond lily, it gradually moved out of sight and was seen no more.... Finally, one of the waterbugs, a leader in the colony, gathered its friends together. "I have an idea," he said, "the next one of us who climbs up the lily stalk must promise to come back and tell us where he or she went and why."

One spring day, not long after, the very waterbug who had suggested the plan found himself climbing up the lily stalk. Up, up, up he went. Before he knew what was happening, he had broken through the surface of the water, and had fallen onto the broad, green lily pad above. When he awoke, he looked about with surprise. He couldn't believe what he saw. A startling change had come to his old body. His movement revealed four silver wings and a long tail.... The dragonfly remembered the promise he had made when he had been a waterbug: "The next one of us who climbs up the lily stalk will come back and tell where she went and why."

Without thinking, the dragonfly started down. Suddenly he hit the surface of the water and bounced away. Now that he was a dragonfly he could no longer go into the water. "I can't return!" he said in dismay. "At least I tried, but I cannot keep my promise. Even if I could go back, not one of the waterbugs would know me in my new body. I guess I will just have to wait until they become dragonflies too. Then they'll understand what happened to me, and where I went."

And the dragonfly winged off happily into its wonderful new world of sun and air.

SIGNS

I often dreamed of my daughter, Michelle, after she lost her life at the age of twenty in a car accident. One of the most beautiful dreams I had of Michelle was when she was writing to me across the sky. Her skywriting messages were scrawled so fast and furiously through the clouds that, like a movie in fast forward, I couldn't make out most of what she was writing. Only two messages were crystal clear. Amidst the clouds she wrote..."*The opportunities are limitless*" and "*The Love Team.*"

In the same dream she was sending me little "love notes" that I was finding everywhere. Wherever I looked, I found these endearing notes. Though I couldn't decipher them, I could *feel* her love.

Within days of having this dream an incredible thing happened. I was busy working at my desk and searching for something in a drawer, when I found an old post-it pad with a note on the top. The note was from Michelle! In her handwriting there was a heart and her name...the way she always wrote *Love Michelle*.

This dream was one of many that I had after Michelle's accident. Almost immediately I began experiencing unusual things that I intuitively felt were *signs*. Many were related to electricity (flickering lights, my car beeping, the smoke alarm), songs on the radio, birds and butterflies. I wanted so badly to believe that life existed after death and that I would see Michelle again, that I opened to the possibility. The more I opened, the more signs and dream messages I received.

On January 25, 2000, the eight-year anniversary of Michelle's tragic passing, my husband suffered a fatal heart attack. He was the only person in the world who could truly understand the pain and devastation of losing Michelle. Each day I prayed for him to come to me to let me know that they were together and that something more existed.

One morning as I awoke, I heard the dresser drawers open and close as though my husband was getting ready for work. Suddenly, I felt him kiss my forehead. My eyes flew open!

There he was at the foot of my bed, wearing a red golf shirt with his hair slicked back as though he just got out of the shower. He looked young and healthy and smiled at me..

I grabbed him and shouted, *Do you have her?* He said *Yes* and pointed to my right. There on the other side of the bed was Michelle. I wrapped my arms around her and through my sobs I heard her say, *Daddy, tell her why we're here.*

I turned back to my husband and now he was sweating, as though he had worked very hard to reach me. He said, *Even though Michelle and I are here and you are there with our other children, we are still a family and I will continue to look over you.*

And then they began to fade. I got out of bed and went into Michelle's room where my other daughter now slept. She was awake. I said to her, *I just saw Daddy and Michelle.* She said, *I did, too!*

Then the phone rang. And I suddenly felt myself being pulled back into my body which was lying in bed. I didn't know if I'd had a dream visitation or an out-of-the-body experience? Whether they came to me or I went to them?

And in the end, it really didn't matter.

> — Lilly Julien
> Founder & President of COPE Foundation

Perhaps they are not the stars,
but rather openings in Heaven
where the love of our lost ones
pours through
and shines down upon us
to let us know
they are
happy.

— inspired by an Eskimo legend

TO BELIEVE OR NOT TO BELIEVE

During daily meditations, my late wife, Joy, whom I'd been grieving, appeared increasingly real in my mind's eye. One time she became so palpably real, I could almost *feel* her. Then, at the end of one blissful communion, something extraordinary happened—she *kissed* me. It was so "real" I swear I felt it!

In the moment, I was enraptured by Joy's kiss. But for the rest of the day and the days that followed I realized I'd been shaken by the reality of it. Throughout these past months and despite many "contacts" with Joy, I still wasn't sure whether I was experiencing self-induced hallucinations or an actual spiritual reality. And I was happy to sit on the fence and not question it too closely. But for some reason this kiss provoked me. Was it *really* real?

I remembered a story I'd written years earlier, before I met Joy, and rummaged through my files until I found it. As I read my heart sank. This long forgotten story disturbed me deeply because it seemed I was living out some fantasy I'd created long ago.

I became disillusioned. I'd always considered the possibility that these "contacts" with Joy were imaginary. Now I was certain I'd made the whole thing up—imagined these experiences to console myself. I stopped meditating. I couldn't endure another imaginary embrace.

I went into a tailspin. No longer able to score my drug of choice—"contact" with Joy—I could no longer numb my pain by imagining that somehow, albeit supernaturally, we were still together.

I was desolate. I felt like a fool. Like I'd been fooled. I felt pathetic. A fraud. The levees I'd built from my "contacts" with Joy had been breached, and I was drowning in the flood of my unadulterated grief now compounded by scathing self- recrimination.

Though despondent, I couldn't cry. And that made matters worse. *What's the matter with me that I can't cry?* Something in me had hardened or I'd fallen so far down into a well of sadness that my tears couldn't reach the surface. My voice thickened, my eyes stung. But tears didn't flow.

I walked around the lake near my home hoping for some comfort, perhaps even some answers. With its water, trees, and bird life, the lake was a place of renewal, but also a place of painful memories. The lake's pastoral beauty attracted couples young and old. Whether I passed an old couple seated on a bench holding hands watching the world go by, or a young couple sprawled on the grass, wrapped in an embrace, oblivious to the world around them, I was reminded of Joy and the thousands of times we had enjoyed ourselves at the lake.

I often cried at the lake, especially when I listened to certain songs on my iPod. So it was doubly upsetting to walk the lake during my "grief relapse" and listen to those songs, but not be able to cry.

One day the sky above the lake was filled with an unusual cloud formation. It looked like a phalanx of angels—an "angel brigade"—which I hoped was a good omen.

I returned home to discover emergency roadwork in front of my building. Inside my condo the noise was still quite loud, so I closed all the windows to muffle the deafening jackhammers. But the vibrations rattled the windows. My home office faced the street and I couldn't stay in it because of the din. To get away from the racket, I moved from one room to the next, away from the street, until I found myself in the quietest spot of all—Joy's walk-in closet.

Joy's closet was the last place I wanted to be. Like everyone who's lost a spouse, I'd been grappling with the issue of what to do with her things. Every time I'd step into her closet, a searing wave of grief would sweep over me and I'd back out as if I'd been physically expelled. Then I'd tell myself that I wasn't ready to go through all of her neatly organized clothes. Not yet.

So Joy's closet was the last place I expected to find myself. But since the closet was the quietest place I could find, I decided to spend some time just looking at a few things.

I began by smelling her clothes. Then I sniffed her jewelry, which still held the scent of her perfume. I touched her silk blouses and velvet pants, holding them up to my nose and cheek. I soon became intoxicated, and slowly, without realizing it, began going through her clothing.

Over the next few hours I touched every piece of Joy's clothing—blouses jackets, dresses, pants, shoes, hats, handbags, even her jewelry and belts. To my surprise, I began to find tissues in the pockets of her pants and jackets. Lots and lots of tissues. *Why so many tissues?*

Then I remembered that whenever we dined out, after finishing her meal, she'd blot her newly applied lipstick with tissues. And I began to whimper. Each pocket held neatly folded unused tissues. A pile began to form on the floor. I began to sob. It was the strangest thing—every pocket's stash of tissues seemed to evoke more tears from me. So I began to wipe my eyes and blow my nose with each new tissue, and then throw it on top of the growing pile. It was uncanny, as if the tissues needed to be used because I needed to shed tears.

Hours flew by. I emptied dozens and dozens and dozens of pockets of their tissues. And I cried and cried...until I'd emptied every pocket and there were no more tissues and no more tears. Perhaps I was delirious, but the pile of tissues strewn on the floor of the closet now bore an uncanny resemblance to the "angel brigade" of clouds I'd seen earlier in the day.

When I finally emerged from Joy's closet it was dark outside. And quiet. The construction had stopped. I called a friend and told him what had happened—that I'd been so depressed I couldn't even cry, and about the angel brigade of clouds that had appeared in the sky, and the emergency road work that drove me into Joy's closet where I found tissues that made me cry and feel better. I wondered aloud if I was being looked after by Joy? Or was it simply my wishful imagination again?

To which my wise friend replied, "Why don't you just accept it as an unexpected gift."

The next day, my morning reading in the book, *Healing After Loss* by Martha Whitmore Hickman, had this sage advice:

"Whether it is our own projection or, in some way, the visiting spirit of our loved one, we have no way of knowing. We would like it to be our loved one—some contact, some assurance of continuing life. But oddly enough, perhaps it doesn't matter a great deal. If we are comforted, let's be grateful for that. And if this easing of the spirit comes from our own imagination— well, the Creator of life gave us our imagination, too."

So it didn't take me long to start "using" again. My withdrawal from the spiritual comfort of "contact" with Joy didn't last long. A few days later, another quote from my morning reading in *Healing After Loss* helped me rationalize "falling off the wagon" of sober rationality and skeptical cynicism.

"We who have stood at the doorway of death, watching our loved one pass through, are entitled to all flights of imagination as we contemplate the unknown."

— adapted from *JOYride: How My Late Wife Loved Me Back To Life* by I. J. Weinstock

Death is not extinguishing the light;
it is putting out the lamp because the dawn has come.

— Rabindranath Tagore

Death is only an experience through which you are meant to learn
a great lesson: you cannot die.

— Yogananda

While we are mourning the loss of our friend,
others are rejoicing to meet him behind the veil.

— John Taylor

Death ends a life, not a relationship.

— Morrie Schwartz, *Tuesdays With Morrie*

CONGRATULATIONS

Congratulations on completing the *Grief Quest* workbook. It took courage to embark on this quest. I hope that answering the L.O.V.E. questions has helped you find an outlet for your grief and a container for your loving memories.

Others who've completed their *Grief Quest* have found benefit in reviewing their journal and journey. Reading what they had written inspired them to add to their answers. Memories fuel more memories.

YOUR ON-GOING GRIEF QUEST,,,,

For many of you, 28 days will not be enough. It certainly wasn't nearly enough for all the questions I had. I could have filled several workbooks.

For many, completing the workbook will be just the beginning. As someone who came to the end of the workbook told me—

> *"I would love to have a sequel workbook to continue writing in. 28 days is great, but not nearly enough! This could be a 3 or 6 month program!"*

To meet that need, I'm developing an online *Grief Quest*, so that you can continue the process for as long as you want and as frequently as you wish.

For more information about how to continue your *Grief Quest*, write to GriefQuest@gmail.com

YOUR FEEDBACK IS IMPORTANT!

Sharing your Grief Quest experience will help make future editions of the workbook an even more effective and powerful tool for those grieving the loss of their loved one. For example:

- *Did you do the workbook on a daily basis? Or sporadically?*

- *Which of the L.O.V.E questions were easiest, hardest and most impactful?*

- *How did completing the Grief Quest workbook affect you?*

Send your comments and feedback to GriefQuest@gmail.com.

ABOUT THE AUTHOR

I. J. "Jerry" Weinstock is the son of Holocaust survivors. During his varied career, he's been an actor, artist, producer and author. In the 80's, his groundbreaking book about women was featured on the *The Donahue Show* (the Oprah of its time). In the 90's, his cable network, The Game Channel, was the precursor to GSN (The Game Show Network).

When Jerry lost his wife, Joy, to breast cancer, he was devastated. But a remarkable thing happened—Joy began communicating with him from the Afterlife. Over the course of a year, she led him on an incredible journey to heal his grief. Inspired by his extraordinary experience, he wrote a memoir, *JOYride: How My Late Wife Loved Me Back To Life*, which has won an eLit Award—the Silver Medal for Best *Inspirational/Spiritual* Digital Book of 2011.

He has written several books about how to heal from the loss of a loved one: *Grief Quest: A Workbook & Journal to Heal the Grieving Heart*, and (with Lilly Julien) *Grief Quest: A Workbook & Journal to Heal the Parent's Grieving Heart*.

He has presented workshops at the national and international conferences of The Compassionate Friends, and works with the bereaved as a *grief guide*.

He can be reached at GriefQuest@gmail.com.

LOVE

Notes

LOVE

Notes

LOVE

Notes

Notes

64429894R00064

Made in the USA
Middletown, DE
29 August 2019